In memory of Dylan. A wonderful little boy, who
enriched so many of our lives, loved stories and
will remain in my heart always.

Neil x

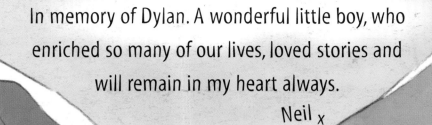

Red Robin Books is an imprint of Corner To Learn Limited

Published by

Corner To Learn Limited

Willow Cottage ● 26 Purton Stoke ● Swindon ● Wiltshire SN5 4JF ● UK

ISBN: 978-1-905434-26-8

First published in the UK 2009

Text © Neil Griffiths 2009

Illustrations © Janette Louden 2009

Design by David Rose

Printed in China by PrintWORKS

SNEEZY BEAR

Neil Griffiths

Illustrated by
Janette Louden

Bear was enjoying a nice **cool** soak!
In fact, he would have soaked all day
long if he hadn't begun to feel **hungry**.

He spotted some plump silver salmon.
"M...m...mmmm!" he mumbled,
as his tummy **rumbled.**

Then he saw a tree full of
juicy red cherries!
"**Yummy**," he mumbled,
as his tummy
rumbled.

But then, bear found a bush full of ripe blueberries.
"Scrummy!"
he mumbled, as his tummy rumbled.

"Oh dear, dear, dear," sighed bear.

Next, bear saw an ant hill full of his favourite tiny ants. "**Oooo!**" he mumbled, as his tummy **rumbled**.

Aaaaatishoo!

Bear lay down in the cool
shade of a tree. He just had to
stop sneezing, or he would never
get any food in his tummy.

Aaaaa...

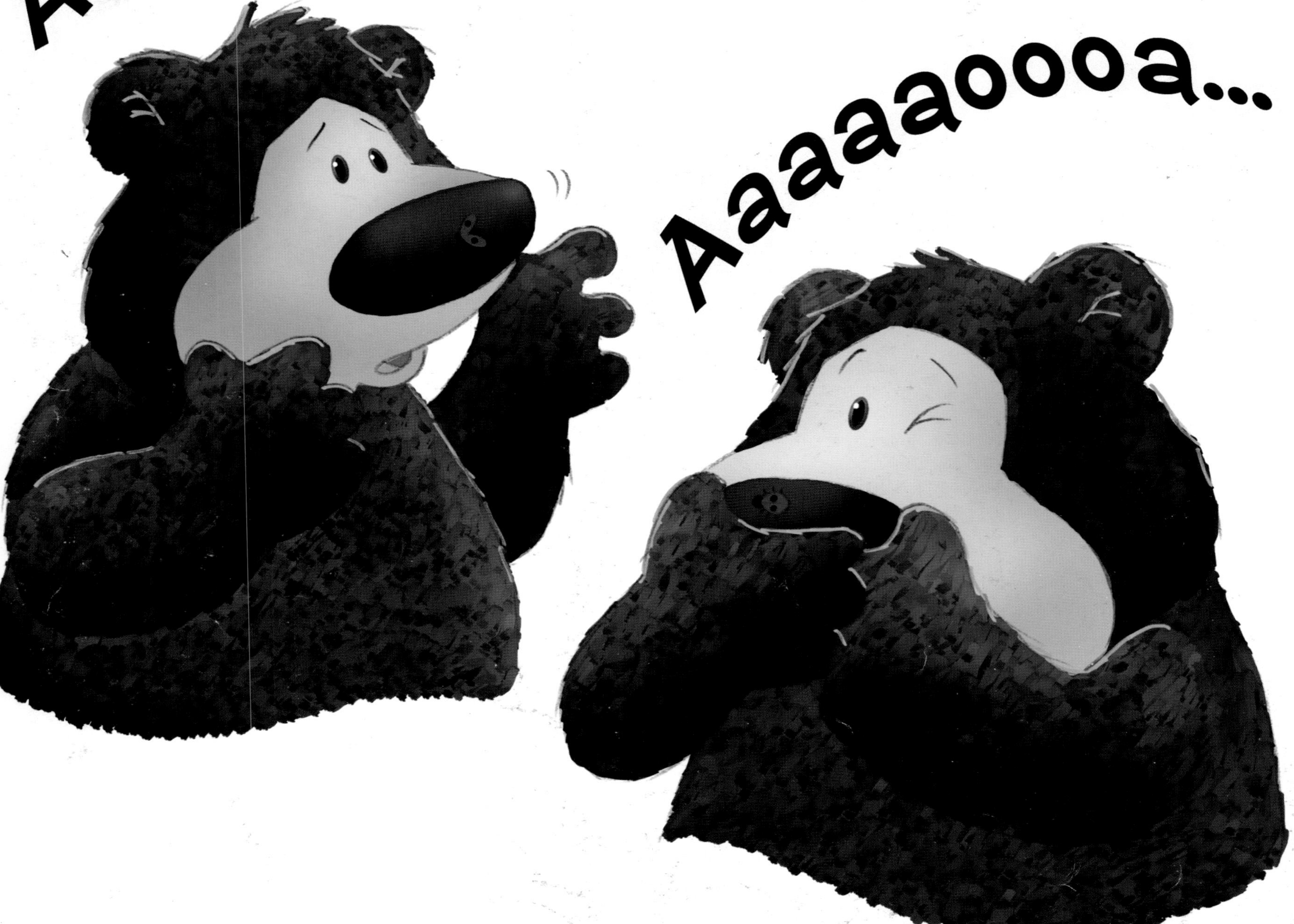

Aaaaaoooa...